MC CESAR

TOMMY DONBAVAND

Illustrated by Mark Penman

MC Cesar ISBN 978-1-78464-441-3

Text © Tommy Donbavand 2016
Complete work © Badger Publishing Limited 2016

Publisher: Susan Ross
Senior Editor: Danny Pearson
Editorial Coordinator: Claire Morgan
Copyeditor: Cheryl Lanyon
Designer: Bigtop Design Ltd
Illustrator: Mark Penman

2 4 6 8 10 9 7 5 3 1

Contents

CHAPTER 1

CESAR

My best friend was born on the same day as me.

His name is Julian Cheese.

We started school together, and always hung around together.

We were both really into music.

We spent hours and hours downloading songs and mixing them together.

Kids at school used to buy our cool mix CDs for a fiver each.

Then, one day, the head teacher called us
to his office. He had heard about us selling
CDs in the playground.

We thought we were going to get into
trouble. But we didn't.

"I'd like you two boys to run this year's
school disco," he said.

That first kids' disco was when Julian Cheese
changed his DJ name to MC Cesar.

CHAPTER 2
STAR

MC Cesar became famous after our first few school discos.

Our mix songs got played on the radio. Cesar was interviewed on local TV. The local newspaper even wrote a story about him.

I was there too, of course. But people didn't want to talk to me – plain old Mark Anthony. They thought MC Cesar was the star.

MC Cesar always wore a black cap with a gold leaf pattern, and he even paid the biggest kid at our school – Bob 'The Brute' Briscoe – to be his bodyguard!

"You should get yourself a cool name like mine," Cesar said.

But I knew I'd feel stupid if I went around pretending I was all important, like he did.

CHAPTER 3
MARCH

So I followed MC Cesar around, carrying his kit while he got all the fans. We started playing at a real nightclub called The Capitol once a week.

"I've invited some of the kids from school to see us," Cesar told me one day.

"But they're all too young to get in!" I said.

"Don't worry," said Cesar. "I met a guy called Joey March. He's going to sell them all fake IDs and share the profits with us!"

I didn't like the sound of that.

I'd heard that Joey March used kids to sneak drugs into nightclubs. We could get into a lot of trouble.

"Beware the IDs of March!" I told Cesar.

But he didn't listen to me.

CHAPTER 4
HAVOC

That night, The Capitol nightclub was busier than ever.

The place was packed with underage kids who had got in with their fake IDs.

I could see them passing out small packets of drugs. They collected money and took it to Joey March.

I was worried, but MC Cesar didn't seem to notice. He started to play our latest mix song – *Cry Havoc.*

The crowd pushed forwards, but The Brute got in their way.

"Stay back!" he ordered. "No one gets near MC Cesar!"

Then the doors crashed open and the police burst in.

They knew about the kids passing drugs around and wanted to know who had arranged for them to get fake IDs.

Everyone pointed to MC Cesar.

CHAPTER 5
DECKS

The music stopped playing and the police put handcuffs on MC Cesar.

"You're under arrest," said one of the officers.

"Get him out of my club!" said Jim Casca, the manager.

"Drugs?" said The Brute, shocked. "You're on your own, mate."

"You too, Brute?" cried Cesar.

Joey March was arrested too, and all the underage kids were sent home.

But that still left loads of ravers waiting for the music to start again.

"Looks like it's down to you, Mark!" said Jim Casca.

I stepped up to the DJ decks. Cesar had taken his headphones with him, so I needed to borrow a pair.

"Friends, ravers, club-entry men," I said, "lend me your earphones!"

STORY FACTS

This story is based on one of my favourite Shakespeare plays, Julius Caesar.

In the play, Caesar is given more and more power by the Roman people. He begins to believe that he can never be defeated. But all the while, others are plotting to kill him and take his place.

For this story, I swapped Ancient Rome for a modern-day nightclub. Julius Caesar became MC Cesar, who also believed he was too important to get into any trouble.

I even took some of Shakespeare's quotes from the play and changed them to fit in the story. Here are the originals – can you spot my versions?

"Beware the Ides of March."

"Et tu, Brute?"

"Friends, Romans, countrymen – lend me your ears."

Tommy Donbavand

QUESTIONS

What is MC Cesar's real name?
(page 10)

What is the name of MC Cesar's bodyguard?
(page 14)

What is on MC Cesar's special hat?
(page 14)

Who does MC Cesar get fake IDs from?
(page 16)

What is the name of Cesar and Mark's
latest song?
(page 22)

Tommy Donbavand has written over 80 books for children. Most of them are so scary that you have to sleep with the lights on after reading them! His 13-book Scream Street series has been made into a CBBC TV series. Recently, he wrote his first Doctor Who novel, *Shroud of Sorrow*. Tommy lives in Lancashire with his wife, two sons and more and more pets!

Mark Penman thinks he maybe played one too many fantasy games on his computer. Now it seems he can only silence the horrifying voices in his head by drawing scary stories starring terrified teens.